M000026318

# NATIVE AMERICANS

## Projects, Games, and Activities
### FOR GRADES 4-6

**Barbara Adams**

**Troll Associates**

**Interior Illustrations by Keith Neely**

Copyright © 1994 by Troll Associates.  All rights reserved.
Permission is hereby granted to the purchaser to reproduce,
in sufficient quantities to meet yearly student needs,
pages bearing the following statement:
© 1994 by Troll Associates.

ISBN:  0-8167-3334-1

Printed in the United States of America.
10   9   8   7   6   5   4   3   2   1

# CONTENTS

# TO THE TEACHER

Native Americans had been living and thriving in North America for thousands of years before European explorers and colonists arrived to stake their claims in the "New World." What was life like for these Native Americans before contact with the Europeans? Where did they live? How did they adapt to the environment? How did they use natural resources? What were their beliefs, customs, and traditions? You and your students will discover answers to these and many other questions as you explore twelve Native American tribes from different regions of the United States and Canada.

**NATIVE AMERICANS:** Projects, Games, and Activities for Grades 4-6 is designed to supplement your existing curricula. The projects, games, and activities are enjoyable and simple to do, requiring only readily available materials. You will even find suggestions for gathering natural materials and using them as Native Americans once did. Interesting and informative background pages, read-aloud myths and legends, and descriptions about Native American children and their families introduce students to various beliefs, customs, and traditions. Exploring these different Native American cultures will help your students respect, appreciate, and understand those who came before.

**NATIVE AMERICANS:** Projects, Games, and Activities for Grades 4-6 is organized into sections, or cultural regions, so named for the climate, topography, or location being discussed. The regions included are the Northeast Woodlands, the Southeast, the Great Basin, the Plains, the Southwest, the Northwest Coast, and the Subarctic and Arctic.

# NATIVE AMERICANS AND WHERE THEY LIVED

Native Americans once lived all over North America. This map shows the geographic areas where the tribes presented in this book originally made their homes.

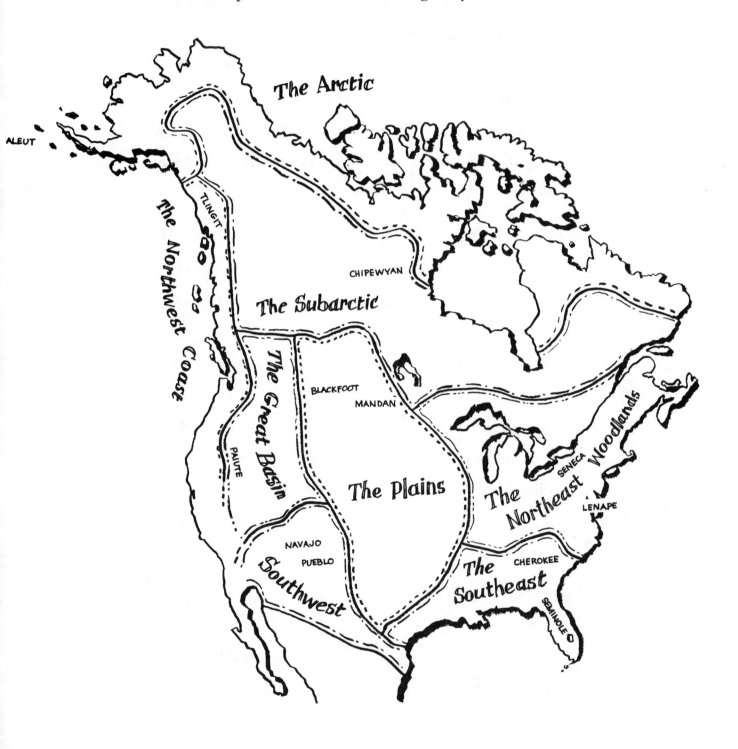

# THE LAND AND PEOPLE OF THE
# NORTHEAST WOODLANDS

The Northeast Woodlands stretch from the Atlantic Ocean to the Mississippi River and from the Great Lakes to the Carolinas and into Tennessee. Although the land varies—coast, lakes, mountains, and valleys—the forest is the one constant. Scores of tribes—Algonquian, Iroquois, and some Sioux—thrived in this fertile environment. They hunted deer, bears, moose, wild ducks, geese, partridge, beavers, and other game. They cleared land to plant corn, beans, and squash. They gathered nuts, berries, roots, and wild plants. River, coast, and lake tribes also fished. Some gathered clams and shellfish. The trees of the forest provided the materials the tribes needed for their dwellings, canoes, tools, utensils, and fuel.

# MEET THE
# SENECA

**D**uring the early 1400s in what is now New York State, five tribes—the Cayuga, Mohawk, Oneida, Onondaga, and Seneca—joined to form the *Iroquois League,* or *Five Nations.* The Seneca were the largest of the tribes. They lived in the westernmost part of Iroquois territory and were known within the League as the *Keepers of the Western Door.*

The Seneca, like the other Iroquois, built villages on hills near rivers or streams. To clear the land, they burned the trees at their bases. Doing so provided open areas from which to spot approaching enemies. The cleared land was also useful for growing crops. The Seneca used the felled wood to construct a *palisade*, a fence of tall stakes that protected the village from attack, and *long houses*, the rectangular dwellings in which they lived. As many as a dozen related families might share a long house, and each would have its own area for sleeping and storing possessions and food. The long houses had no windows, only smoke holes for the fires that burned along the center corridor.

Seneca warriors were often away on long military and trading expeditions to expand their territory and fur trade. They also hunted. Most other responsibilities were left to the women. They looked after the old, nurtured the young, and tended the corn, squash, bean, and sunflower crops. Women also played other important roles. They nominated the men who were to represent their tribe at the "great council," a governing body consisting of members from each tribe in the Iroquois League. The women could also remove any members of the great council who were not fulfilling their responsibilities. Furthermore, the oldest woman in every long house was head of the household. She owned all the property, from the tools to the dwelling. When she died, the next oldest female relative took her place.

Seneca children were treated lovingly but were not spoiled. They were taught to eat healthfully and frugally. They were toughened with cold water baths. At about the age of eight, children began to learn more about their duties. Girls performed chores in the long house or worked in the fields with the older women. Groups of boys were allowed to go off into the woods for days, eating berries, roots, and any small game they caught with bow and arrow or blowgun. Boys were also allowed to join a hunting party with the men once they had killed a deer by themselves. As boys grew older, they had to prove themselves in other ways before they could become warriors. Thus, from an early age each Seneca child learned the responsibilities he or she would have someday in the adult Seneca community.

# The Race Between Turtle and Beaver

The turtle is special to Native Americans and appears in many creation stories. It is usually characterized as a clever animal capable of outsmarting bigger and faster animals.

Turtle lived in a pond that was small and not very deep. Day after day, Turtle swam, napped in the sun, and ate fish. One day, a cold north wind began to blow. Turtle knew that it was time to sleep.

Turtle swam to the bottom of his pond and made a bed for himself in the soft mud. There he fell asleep for the winter. When at last he woke up, Turtle began swimming to the top. But the trip took longer than usual. The water was deeper than when he had gone to sleep!

Turtle looked about. His pond was not only deeper but also much bigger. The trees had been cut down to make a dam. Turtle saw a strange-looking animal with a large, flat tail swimming his way.

Turtle asked, "Who are you? Why are you in *my* pond? What did you do to *my* trees?"

The animal answered, "I'm Beaver and this is *my* pond. *I* cut down the trees with my very sharp teeth to build a dam."

Turtle said, "*You* are mistaken. This is *my* pond, and I will fight you if you don't leave."

Beaver agreed to fight.

After looking at Beaver's long, sharp teeth, Turtle said, "It would be too easy for me to fight you. Let's have a contest. The loser must leave the pond forever."

Beaver agreed. He said, "Let's see which of us can stay under the water the longest. *I* can stay under for a whole day."

When Turtle heard that, he knew he had to think of a different contest. He said, "It would be too easy for me to win. Let's race to the other side of the pond. Whoever loses must leave the pond forever."

Beaver said, "Of all the animals who swim, I am the fastest. Let's begin."

Turtle thought quickly. He said, "Wait! Because I, too, am a fast swimmer, let me start the race behind you." So Turtle got in back of Beaver next to his big tail.

As the race began, Turtle bit into Beaver's tail. But Beaver did not look back. He just swam harder and faster, swinging his tail

from side to side. Turtle did not let go. When Beaver had almost reached the other side, Turtle bit down harder. This time when Beaver flipped his tail into the air, Turtle let go. There went Turtle, sailing through the air and crossing the finish line first. Beaver stared in disbelief and then sadly waddled away from the grassy bank, never to return.

"It's good to have my pond back," Turtle said, smiling, as he munched on a delicious minnow.

# Making a Bowl Game

For the Iroquois, late January or early February marked the end of the year. At that time, they held a week-long ceremony of thanksgiving and renewal called the "Ceremonial of Midwinter." On the last day of the ceremony, everyone played the Sacred Bowl Game. They used a wooden bowl decorated with the four clan symbols—the bear, wolf, turtle, and deer. In the bowl, they placed six peach pits, each painted white on one side and black on the other. A player hit the bowl sharply against the ground. If five of the six pits turned up the same color, the player scored and took another turn. Show students the picture of the bowl below. Have students make their own versions of the Iroquois Sacred Bowl Game.

## Materials:

6 peach pits, plum stones, or flat unshelled nuts
  for each student
black and white paint
several inexpensive paintbrushes to share
several small cardboard boxes with lids

## What students do:

1. Paint one side of each pit black and the other side white.

2. Pair up with another student.

3. One student in the pair puts all his or her painted pits in the box, covers it, then shakes it up and down.

4. The student removes the lid and observes the pits. If at least 5 pits are the same color, the player scores one point and goes again. If not, the next player takes a turn.

5. The first player to reach 10 points wins the game.

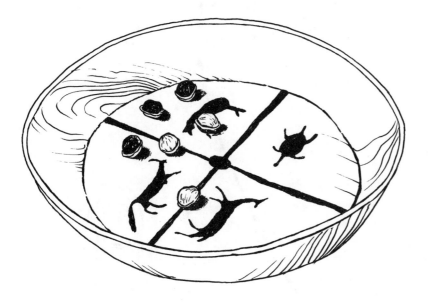

Name _____ Date _____

# Designing a
# False Face Mask

An ill or injured Seneca tribe member sometimes asked the False Face Society to drive away the spirit of the illness or injury.  A False Face mask has been started for you.  Use colored pencils or crayons to finish it.

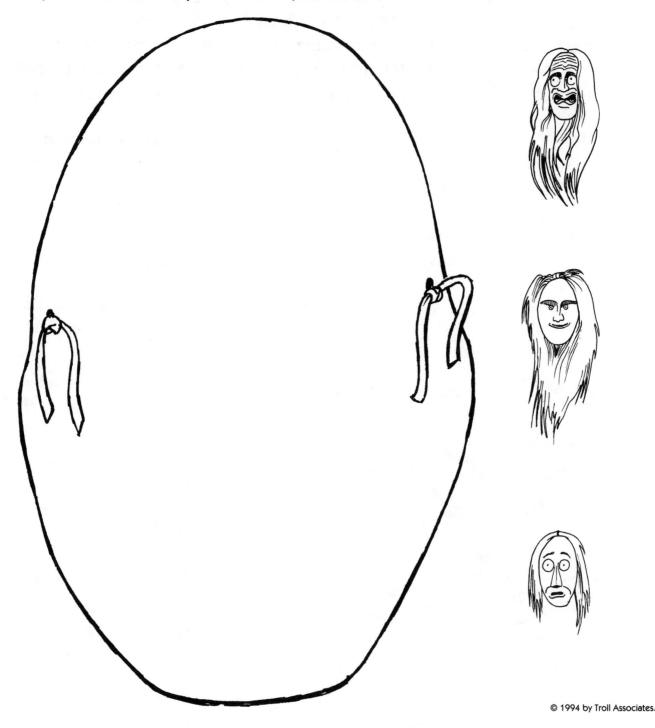

© 1994 by Troll Associates.

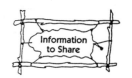
# MEET THE
# LENAPE

**B**efore European settlers arrived, an area called Lenapehoking covered southern New York, eastern Pennsylvania, and all of New Jersey and Delaware. The land varied from ocean beaches and marshlands, to forests, fertile river valleys, and rocky highlands. The people of Lenapehoking were known as Lenape. In their language, the name meant "ordinary people." The Europeans referred to the Lenape as the Delaware, after the river flowing through their land.

The Lenape grew corn, beans, squash, and tobacco. They hunted deer, bear, and other animals. They fished and gathered wild food. They used stone, wood, bone, horn, shell, and sinew to make tools and weapons. They used their tools to build their dwellings, to make dugout canoes, and to craft their bows, arrows, bowls, and utensils. They made their own clothing—breechcloths for men, wraparound skirts for women, and belts, leggings, and moccasins for both—from tanned elk and deer hides and decorated the clothing with shells, stones, seeds, paint, dyes, and porcupine quills. To keep warm in winter, they made fur-lined shawls and wove turkey down robes.

Inheritance passed from mother to daughter. Even the role of *sachem*, or chief, a position held by males, was passed down not to the sachem's son but to a male relative of the sachem's mother.

The Lenape lived in a network of related but independent villages. They built bark-and-grass-covered long houses or round, domed *wigwams*. Sometimes wigwams were oblong and arched, but all dwellings had a large hole in the middle of the roof for the fires that smoldered inside. The Lenape stored food in *silos*, which they dug deep in the ground, lined with marsh grass, and covered with bark. A typical Lenape  village also had a *sweathouse*, a low, windowless structure made of stakes and mud, built near a stream. These sweathouses resembled modern saunas.

The women cared for the children, tended the crops, gathered wild foods, cooked, and made pottery, baskets, and clothing. The men made tools and weapons, hunted, cut down trees, prepared the soil for planting, fished, traded, and fought when necessary. Some men and some women were trained to become *meteinuwak*, or medicine people.

# The Daily Life of a Lenape Girl

Laughing Deer is a Lenape who lives in a small coastal village. During the spring when salmon, herring, and shad swim upstream, many Lenape families gather in camps near the rapids and waterfalls. Laughing Deer watches as her father, uncles, and brothers work the nets and spear the fish. She and her mother and the other women set up the racks to smoke-dry the fish. Although the snows and icy winds of winter are far away, everyone works together to build up their stores of food.

As summer nears, Laughing Deer and her family move to a small community at the edge of the forest where the soil is rich. The time has come to plant crops, but first the men must clear the land. Using stone axes, Laughing Deer's father, uncles, and brothers cut down trees and brush. The men then break up the ground so the corn, bean, and squash seeds can be planted among the stumps. As the days and weeks pass, Laughing Deer helps tend the crops. The village holds a special ceremony with prayers for a good harvest. Also during the summer months, Laughing Deer helps gather berries and other wild foods, while her brothers and father hunt deer, elk, turkey, and other game.

When summer turns to autumn, the village must harvest and dry the crops. Laughing Deer helps her mother cut the squash into strips and braid the cornhusks and bean stems together. Hanging in the warm autumn sun, they will soon dry. Then, Laughing Deer and her mother will store their harvest in the rafters of their wigwam. Laughing Deer is also learning to grind the corn into meal and flour and prepare hominy and succotash. Laughing Deer's tribe will also eat the meat and make clothing from the skins of woodland animals like deer and bear that the adults hunt during this season.

Shorter days and the growing chill signal the coming of winter. Laughing Deer and her family now begin the journey back to their territory. Soon there will be feasting and storytelling, singing and dancing, and thanksgiving for the past year's bounty. The year has been good for Laughing Deer, her family, and her people.

# Making Pottery

The Lenape made clay pots and bowls. To make patterns and designs, they pressed corncobs, nuts, and pebbles onto the wet clay. Students can make their own pottery the same way the Lenape did. It is called the coil method.

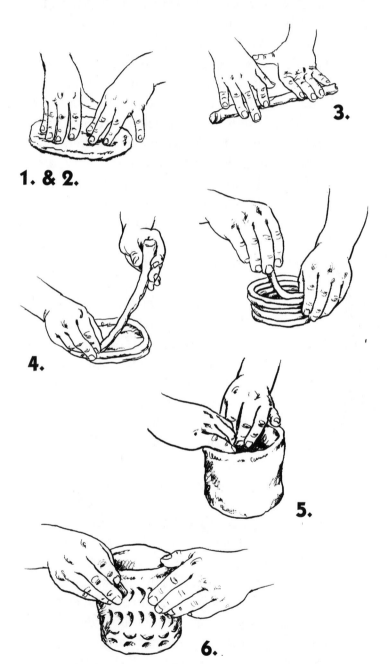

1. & 2.

4.

5.

6.

## Materials:

clay

natural materials such as bark, twigs, and nutshells to create patterns and designs

## What students do:

1. Knead the clay to soften it.

2. Flatten some clay to form a base for the pottery about the size of a drinking cup.

3. Roll the remaining clay into coils of equal length.

4. Lay the coils around the edge of the base, one on top of another.

5. Use hands to smooth the inside and outside surfaces of the pottery.

6. Press and scratch designs into the sides with bark, twigs, and nutshells.

7. Let the pottery dry in the sun or fire it in a kiln if one is available. Note: Pots are for decorative purposes only, not for eating or drinking.

Answers to "Algonquian Word Search" on page 17: toboggan, skunk, hickory, hominy, moccasin, moose, succotash, tomahawk, raccoon, papoose, woodchuck, wampum

Name _____ Date _____

# Algonquian Word Search

The Lenape spoke a language called Algonquian. Many words that we use today came from the Algonquian language. Twelve of these words are hidden in the puzzle. They appear up and down, across, and diagonally. Circle each word as you find it.

```
m   o   c   c   a   s   i   n   c   o
p   k   h   o   m   i   n   y   k   h
w   a   m   p   u   m   s   o   s   i
t   o   p   m   p   o   s   a   k   c
o   h   o   o   o   s   t   o   b   k
m   r   i   d   o   o   s   e   c   o
a   b   a   k   c   s   s   w   m   r
h   m   o   c   o   h   e   e   k   y
a   c   u   a   c   m   u   r   n   o
w   s   b   b   a   o   n   c   u   o
k   c   s   i   n   c   o   y   k   n
t   o   b   o   g   g   a   n   s   r
```

Answers on page 16.

© 1994 by Troll Associates.

# THE LAND AND PEOPLE OF THE
# SOUTHEAST

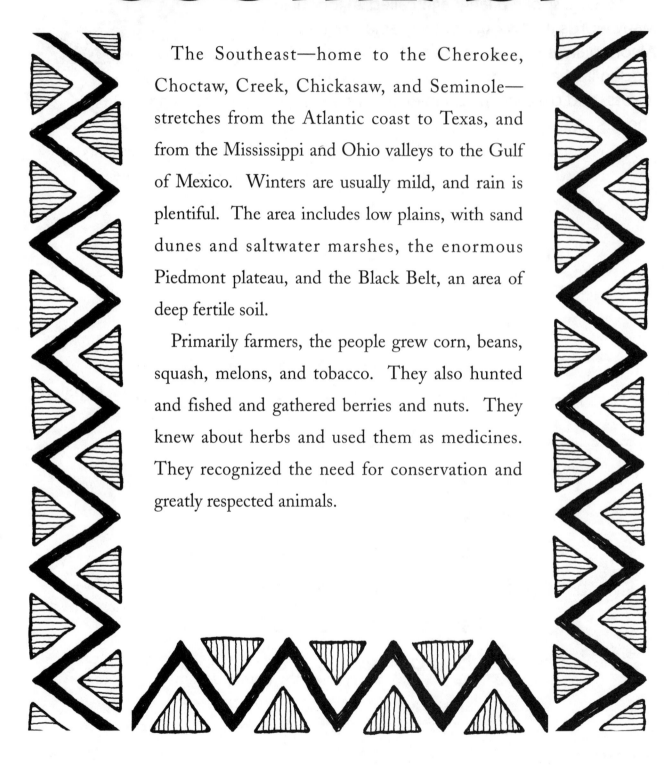

The Southeast—home to the Cherokee, Choctaw, Creek, Chickasaw, and Seminole—stretches from the Atlantic coast to Texas, and from the Mississippi and Ohio valleys to the Gulf of Mexico. Winters are usually mild, and rain is plentiful. The area includes low plains, with sand dunes and saltwater marshes, the enormous Piedmont plateau, and the Black Belt, an area of deep fertile soil.

Primarily farmers, the people grew corn, beans, squash, melons, and tobacco. They also hunted and fished and gathered berries and nuts. They knew about herbs and used them as medicines. They recognized the need for conservation and greatly respected animals.

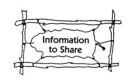

# MEET THE
# SEMINOLE

**D**uring the early 1700s, bands of Creek fled south from Georgia and Alabama to escape the British and tribal wars. Refugees from other Native American tribes, as well as African runaway slaves, also made their way into what is now northern Florida, then controlled by the Spanish. At the time, the region was sparsely populated. Most of the region's inhabitants had either been killed or sold into slavery. Survivors, runaway slaves, and Native American refugees came to be called the Seminole, a name derived from a Spanish word meaning "runaway." Together they created their own culture.

The Seminole lived in small, well-hidden villages. They traveled about the waterways of the swamps in dugout canoes made from cypress trees. Seminole dwellings, called *chickees*, were open-sided, thatch-roofed platforms about three feet (1 m) from the ground. Beneath the roof was a space for storage. Family members slept on floor mats which they rolled up during the day. Babies slept in hammocks.

The Seminole grew corn, pumpkins, sweet potatoes, cowpeas, and sugar cane in small gardens. Bananas, guavas, and other fruits grew wild. The people kept some livestock, especially hogs, but they also hunted alligators, fish, deer, otter, bears, wild turkeys, and many other animals.

Although the swamps were hot and humid, the Seminole kept their bodies covered to protect themselves from swarms of mosquitoes and mites, among other insects. Women wore capelike blouses and decorated cloth skirts that swept the ground. They also wore many strings of beads around their necks, sometimes weighing 25 pounds (11.25 kg). Men dressed in long shirts to the knees or just below. They also wore two bandannas around the neck and a plumed turban to cover their heads. Children dressed like their parents, and everyone went barefoot.

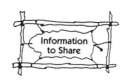

# The Daily Life of a Seminole Boy

Wild Cat lives in a small village in the swamp. Everyone is pleased because a baby has just been born. His name is Little Turtle. Wild Cat watches as his mother ties a small bag of herbs around the baby's neck. She says that the herbs will help chase away bad spirits and keep the baby healthy. Wild Cat glances at his tiny brother who sleeps in the hammock. He thinks about what lies ahead for Little Turtle in the years to come.

As soon as Little Turtle can walk, he will begin to learn the customs and ways of the Seminole. An uncle on his mother's side will

be chosen to train Little Turtle. This uncle will become the boy's counselor and teacher. Little Turtle will be expected to respect his uncle and obey him in every way. This uncle will teach Little Turtle not to lie and to answer only "yes" or "no" when asked a question. The boy will also learn to keep silent when visitors come to the village. Wild Cat remembers how difficult that was!

Little Turtle will have to learn much more. Wild Cat remembers that he had to hunt, fish, and pole a canoe as a very small boy. He even learned how to make a dugout canoe. A huge cypress had fallen during a bad storm. Wild Cat helped the men peel the bark and hollow out the huge trunk after it had dried. Before long, Little Turtle will learn these skills too.

As Little Turtle grows up, he will also discover that not everything is work. Wild Cat still enjoys listening to the storyteller and singing folk songs that have been passed down from his ancestors. He also likes to play stickball. All the boys learn to play as soon as they can run. One day, too, Little Turtle will sing about the little raccoon and the horned owl and play stickball.

Wild Cat is quickly approaching his twelfth year. It's a very important time in his life, for he will no longer be considered a boy, but a man. Wild Cat will soon have all the rights and privileges of the other men in the village. He has learned well. Wild Cat knows that Little Turtle will, too.

Name _____ Date _____

# Telling a Tale

The Seminole often told tales about the stars.  You can, too.  Try writing a story about a Seminole who lost his way on a journey and used the Big Dipper as a boat.

Long ago, a young Seminole set out on a journey.

_____

_____

_____

_____

_____

_____

_____

_____

_____

_____

_____

© 1994 by Troll Associates.

Name _____  Date _____

# Designing a Seminole Shirt

The Seminole wore brightly colored clothing.  A shirt often had strips of compli-
cated designs separated by bands of solid color.  Can you make a design on the
shirt below?  Use crayons to color your design, or cut out and paste on bits of
colored construction paper.

© 1994 by Troll Associates.

# Making a Necklace

When a Seminole girl turned twelve, she was given a strand of glass beads. Each year, she received another strand until her fortieth birthday. After that, a strand of beads was removed each year until she died. Seminole women always wore their beads in public, as not wearing them was considered improper. Show students the picture. Then have them make necklaces for themselves or for someone they know.

## Materials:
pencils
spools of heavy thread
scissors
assorted beads, small buttons, and dry
    macaroni sorted into separate cans
small containers with lids for
    each student (Juice cans with
    covers, deli containers, or egg car-
    tons work well.)

## What students do:
**1.** Select the beads they like and place
   them in their own containers.

**2.** Cut the desired length of thread
   from the spool and tie one end to
   the pencil so that the beads won't slip
   off the thread.

**3.** Begin stringing the beads in an individual design.

**4.** After filling the whole thread, carefully untie the pencil and knot the ends of the
   thread together to make a necklace.

# MEET THE
# CHEROKEE

The mountains and valleys of the southern Appalachians were once the homeland of the *Ani'-Yun'wiya*, the Cherokee. They lived in villages along riverbanks. Each village had a *council house*, a large, circular, windowless building often built on a mound. The walls were made of *wattle*, saplings woven together, and *daub*, a form of mud plaster.

Family homes varied from summer to winter. In summer they lived in large, rectangular wood houses. In winter they moved to an *asi*, a smaller, round, windowless dwelling of wattle and daub. The asi was dark and smoky from the fire, but it was warm. Villagers also built storehouses and cribs for storing crops.

Families had small individual gardens, but villagers also worked together in larger fields in the fertile river valleys. They grew beans, corn, squash, pumpkins, and sunflowers. Women tended the crops, although men sometimes helped clear fields, plant, and harvest. Even elderly women worked. They sat on platforms overlooking the fields and scared away birds and animals that would otherwise eat the crops. Women also gathered firewood, carried water, and cooked the food. They made the benches for their homes as well as pottery and baskets. Women even helped the men prepare the deerskins they would make into clothing.

Men provided meat for their families. In winter, hunting parties using traps, bows and arrows, blowguns, and darts, searched for game. Deer was the most important game animal. The people ate the meat, tanned the hide for clothing, and used the antlers and bones for tools and jewelry, the sinew for thread, and the hooves for glue. The men also hunted bear for the thick fur and for the fat which was made into grease. Claws were used for jewelry. Turkey provided meat for food and feathers for capes.

TURKEY FEATHER CAPE

As in other Native American tribes, the Cherokee traced the family through the female line. A child was not considered related to the father or to the father's mother, sister, or brother. A boy was even trained by his mother's brother instead of his father. When a man married, he lived with his wife along with her mother, her sisters, her sister's children, and her unmarried brothers. Cherokee women were respected within the village, and women of rank could speak freely in the village council.

Name _____ Date _____

# Corn, Corn, Corn

Corn was an important Cherokee crop.  They used it in stew and added it to soup.  They combined corn with other ingredients such as dry beans and chestnuts to make bread.

How many different ways do you eat corn?  List the ways below.

_____

_____

_____

_____

_____

How many products can you find that contain corn?  Read can and package labels.  List the products below.

_____

_____

_____

_____

_____

© 1994 by Troll Associates.

# Planting Seeds

The Cherokee depended on agriculture for some of their food. Corn was of particular importance. Near the end of summer when the late corn crop was ripening, they held a ceremony known as the Green Corn Rite. The people gave thanks for a good harvest. Squash, pumpkins, beans, sunflowers, and gourds were other important crops. Have students plant some of these seeds in window boxes or planters and observe their growth.

## Materials:

corn, squash, pumpkin, bean seeds
potting soil
sand
gravel
organic plant food
window boxes or planters
water

## What students do:

**1.** Add several inches of sand and gravel to the bottom of a planter or window box.

**2.** Add the soil.

**3.** Follow the directions on the packet to plant the seeds.

**4.** Put the planter where it will get sunlight. Regularly water the garden. Check each day to be sure the soil doesn't dry out.

**5.** Add plant food as needed so plants will get the nutrients they need to grow. Read the instructions on the package before using.

Have students keep logs. For each entry, they should note the date and record their observations. Depending upon the season, students may transplant seedlings into home gardens.

Name _____ Date _____

# Making a Monster

A legendary monster called Uktena was sometimes pictured on pottery. It had the forked tongue of a snake, and the wings of a bird. Draw and color your own version of Uktena on this piece of pottery.

© 1994 by Troll Associates.

# Stickball, Anyone?

The Cherokee played a stickball game like lacrosse called *anetsa*. It was sometimes called "the little brother to war" because it could be as violent as a real battle. The field was 230 feet (about 70 m) long, and goalposts were 20 feet (about 6.1 m) high. Players used one or two webbed sticks to toss, catch, and carry the ball. Show students the picture. Have them make their own playing sticks and balls.

## Materials:

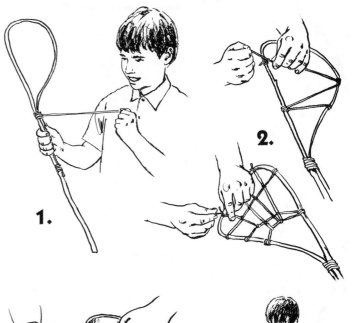

flexible sticks about 3 feet (.91 m) long
  (willow works well)
scissors
twine
newspaper
masking tape

## What students do:

**1.** Tie twine to one end of the stick and bend it to form a loop. Tie it so it will stay bent.

**2.** Crisscross and tie 3 more lengths of twine to make a shallow pocket at the looped end.

**3.** Crumple 3 or 4 sheets of newspaper into a ball and cover it with masking tape.

**4.** Practice tossing and catching the ball with the stick.

Encourage students to devise some version of the Cherokee game and use their sticks to play it.

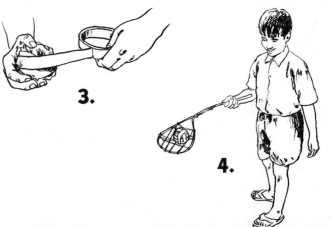

# Performing the Friendship Dance

Dancing was an important part of Native American life. The people performed many different dances for many different reasons. Some were performed to give thanks. Some were to ensure an abundant harvest, good hunting, or victory in battle. Others, such as the friendship dance, were just for fun. Have students learn the dance.

## Materials:

drum
wooden spoon
rattle

(See pages 92 and 93 for instructions on how to make a drum and a rattle.)

## What students do:

**1.** Clear a large area to perform the friendship dance.

**2.** Two students begin by playing a slow steady rhythm with the drum and rattle.

**3.** Two boys stand side by side. They do a slow shuffling step one time around a circle.

**4.** Each boy then asks a girl to join. The four, side by side, then shuffle one time around the circle.

**5.** Each girl then asks a boy to join. The six, still side by side, dance in a circle. The dance continues in this way until everyone joins the dancing circle.

**6.** Then the drummer and rattler change rhythm. At this time, the boys form one circle and the girls another. The two circles then dance in opposite directions. They go around four times to complete the dance.

# THE LAND AND PEOPLE OF THE GREAT BASIN

The Great Basin, a vast desert area, covers most of Utah and Nevada and parts of Colorado, California, Wyoming, Idaho, and Oregon. The basin is almost completely surrounded by uplands—mountains to the east and west and plateaus to the north and southwest. Rainfall is low and evaporation high. Some lakes are salty, and salt flats remain where lakes once existed. The sun scorches the earth in summer. Bitter winds, snow, and storms blast the area in winter. Paiute, Shoshoni, and Ute thrived in this region for centuries. Primarily gatherers, they moved with the seasons, searching for firewood, food, water, and materials for tools and baskets. Mainly, they foraged and dug for food, but they also hunted, farmed, and fished.

Information
to Share

# MEET THE
# PAIUTE

The Paiute of the Great Basin lived in two areas that include parts of Nevada, Utah, California, Oregon, and Arizona. The Paiute in the west inhabited the basin and range terrains, open land divided by mountain ranges. The Paiute in the east lived in the high plateaus and canyons. Bighorn sheep and some antelope ranged through the areas. Jack rabbits, lizards, and desert tortoises were also plentiful.

The Paiute used the available resources well. They farmed the fertile oases, growing corn, squash, melons, pumpkins, sunflowers, and herbs. Some even grew wheat. They planted crops and dug irrigation ditches. They often left their fields for weeks, returning to weed and harvest crops.

The Paiute made seasonal trips to different locations to hunt and gather. In spring they traveled to valleys to gather seeds and greens. In summer they gathered berries, seeds, bulrushes, cattail roots, and flowers. The women used woven *seed beaters* to knock seeds into *burden baskets*. They ground seeds into meal for mush and flat cakes. They also trav-

35

eled into the canyons for cacti, green corn, and spiny flowering plants called *agaves*, all of which they made into large sticky cakes. In late summer and fall, they gathered piñon nuts, which they ground into meal.

The men hunted all year long for large and small game. They tracked larger game in groups and built corrals to trap the animals before shooting them for meat with bows and arrows. The meat was dried and stored for the tribe to eat during the winter when food was scarce.

The Paiute were organized into bands. Their leader was called *niavi* and was always a man, although women held other positions and took part in community meetings. The niavi gave advice and made suggestions, but he had to carry out any council decisions. He was also spokesman for his band.

The Paiute had great respect for the natural world, which they believed was governed by spirits and supernatural beings. Their rites and rituals honored these beings. The Paiute also had special rites and rituals that they observed at the birth of a first child, death, and the passage between childhood and adulthood.

Paiute clothing was very simple. Men wore breechcloths, and women apron-like skirts made from bark or animal skins. Sandals were woven from yucca plants. They sometimes wore hide moccasins. Blankets woven from strips of rabbit skin kept them warm in winter.

# Coyote and the Ocean Grandmother

A Paiute myth tells how people came to live in the Great Basin. Archaeological evidence actually shows that the Paiute arrived in the area about A.D. 1000, probably from southern California with the Paviotso and Shoshoni.

One day, long, long ago, Ocean Grandmother arrived at the home of Wolf and his younger brother Coyote. She had journeyed a great distance out of the west. Wolf noticed that she was carrying a heavy sack. He could also see that the sack was tied tightly. Wolf wondered what was inside but decided not to ask any questions of Ocean Grandmother. Ocean Grandmother then said to Wolf and Coyote, "I want you to carry this sack east to Rabbit's home for me."

Wolf agreed to do as Ocean Grandmother asked, but when she had departed, he said to Coyote, "You take the sack to Rabbit. He will know what to do with it."

Wolf then warned Coyote not to open the sack until he saw Rabbit. So Coyote headed eastward carrying the mysterious sack. As he traveled, he grew more and more curious.

"I wonder what's in this sack," he said to himself. "Maybe Ocean Grandmother filled it with sand or earth to fool us."

While stopping to rest, Coyote decided to examine the sack a little more closely to see if he could figure out what was inside. "Maybe Ocean Grandmother filled it with lizards and snakes," he mumbled to himself. Then he picked up the sack once again and continued eastward toward Rabbit's home.

Coyote only traveled a short distance. Then, unable to control his curiosity any longer, he decided to risk Wolf's anger and untie the sack. There before his eyes, crowds of people began pouring out of the sack, shouting and running in all different directions. Coyote was stunned.

At that moment, Rabbit arrived on the scene. "Why did you open the sack?" he demanded. "This is no place for people to live! You're a fool, Coyote." Rabbit took the few people left inside the sack to the Colorado River on the north side of the Grand Canyon. There they would find plenty to eat, piñon nuts, agaves, and antelope.

After a while when the people who had escaped from the sack had grown accustomed to the new land, they decided they would stay, for they liked it.

**37**

# Making a Model Paiute Home

During the winter months, the Paiute built cone-shaped lodges called *wickiups*. To make the framework, they fastened three or four poles together at the top. Next, they leaned other poles and branches against the frame and covered them with bark, rushes, and other natural materials. In the mid 1800s, they began to use hides and canvas. Show students the picture. Then have them make models. If possible, have them gather their own natural materials.

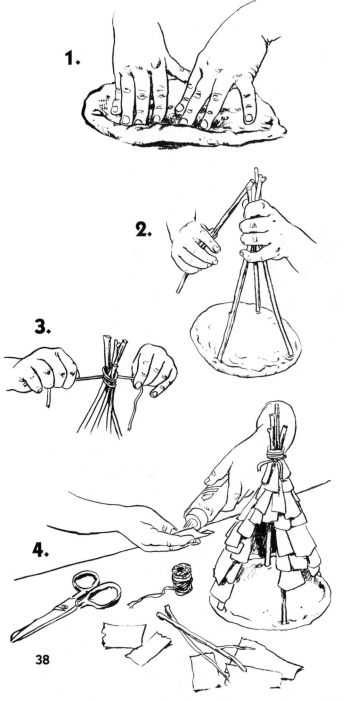

## Materials for each student:

a handful of clay for a base
10-12 sturdy twigs—4 should be 4 inches (about 10 cm) long; the rest should be about 6 inches (about 15 cm) long
dried grasses and weeds or finely shredded paper
dried bark
pieces of brown paper grocery bag
string or twine
scissors
glue

## What students do:

1. Flatten clay into a 4" (10 cm) circular base.

2. Arrange 4 twigs in the clay.

3. Lean sticks against the frame to form the cone-shaped dwelling. Leave an opening for a doorway. Tie sticks at the top.

4. Cover the sides with the dried natural materials or pieces of brown paper bag. Use glue as needed.

# Playing a Paiute Game

The Paiute enjoyed playing games at their winter camps. One was a hand game. To play, two teams sat facing each other. They took turns hiding two pieces of wood or bone in their hands. One piece in each pair had a stripe around the middle. The other was plain. After the pieces were hidden, the other team guessed who was holding the marked and unmarked pieces and in which hand. To keep score, the players used stick counters. The Paiute often played for horses, jewelry, skins, and other goods. Show students the picture. Then have students make their own version of the hand game.

## Materials:

a pair of stones for each student
 (Students may want to bring in
 their own stones.)
paints and paintbrushes to
 share

## What students do:

**1.** Paint a stripe or other design around one of the stones. One stone should not be marked.

**2.** After the stones dry, have students form teams to play the hand game as described above.

# Making Piñon Nut and Sunflower Cakes

Late in the summer and fall, the Paiute gathered piñon nuts from the cones of piñon pine trees. They used poles to knock down opened cones and seeds. If the cones were closed, the women heated them in a fire to open them. Next, the women roasted the nuts by shaking them in a special basket of hot coals. Then they cracked the shells on a *metate* or grinding stone with a *mano* or hand stone. Seeds were then ground into meal and stored for cooking. Have students try this recipe if you have an oven available for class use.

## Materials:
1 cup roughly ground shelled
   sunflower seeds
1 cup roughly ground pine nuts
pinch of salt
1 teaspoon (5 ml) cooking oil
oven foil

## What students do:
**1.** Mix salt into the ground seeds and nuts.

**2.** Add cooking oil.

**3.** Form the mixture into small flat cakes.

**4.** Wrap each cake in foil.

**5.** Bake at 350° F (180° C) for about 30-40 minutes.

**6.** Cool the cakes before eating.

# Making a Petroglyph

Native Americans sometimes made *petroglyphs*, carvings on rocks or boulders. They used hard stones to chip away at the surface of the boulder, making hundreds and thousands of tiny chips to create pictures. Many petroglyphs are of animals and hunters on horseback. Have students make their own versions of petroglyphs.

## Materials:

a variety of clean, dry rocks with flat
surfaces (If possible, take students on
a nature walk to gather rocks, or have
them look for rocks around their yards
and neighborhoods to bring to class.)
chalk

## What students do:

**1.** Think of an animal or other figure to draw.

**2.** Using chalk, make dots, first to outline the figure and then to fill it in.

Display the completed "petroglyphs" and invite the artists to tell about their figures.

# THE LAND AND PEOPLE OF THE
# PLAINS

The Plains stretch from the Mississippi River to the Rocky Mountains and from Canada to Mexico. To the east is a humid area of tall grass prairie. To the west is a drier, short grass region where huge herds of buffalo once grazed. Although mostly grassland, the Plains also have plateaus and buttes, mountains, and fertile river-bank woodlands.

By the 1600s, tribes such as the Mandan and Pawnee lived in villages near rivers and depended on farming for much of their food. They also hunted buffalo. In contrast, tribes like the Blackfoot and Comanche were nomadic hunters who depended almost entirely on the buffalo. They did not farm and did little fishing.

After the coming of horses in the 1600s, and then guns and ammunition, hunting became easier. Many tribes migrated to the Plains, and many former village tribes adopted a nomadic way of life that centered around the horse and buffalo.

# MEET THE
# MANDAN

The Mandan were one of many tribes to migrate to the Plains from other regions of the country. Where they came from originally is not known, but by the 1400s, Mandan were living along the Missouri River. They built their villages on rises overlooking the river. After using up the wood and exhausting the soil in one area, they would move farther upriver and build a new village. Slowly they migrated in this way until they reached what is now North Dakota.

The Mandan constructed *palisades* around their villages. Within the palisades' spiked walls, Mandan built earth lodges around a village plaza. Several related families lived within a lodge. The Mandan stored tools and utensils on the domed roof of the lodge. The roof was also a convenient place to relax, gossip, play games, and even do chores. Inside the lodge, it was dark and smoky, the only light coming from the smoke hole overhead. The men often tethered their horses inside so they would be ready in case of a raid.

As in many other Native American tribes, when a man married, he moved into his wife's lodge. His clothing, weapons, and stallion were his only possessions. Everything else belonged to the woman, including the lodge, the mares, the colts, and the dogs.

In the center of each village, the Mandan erected a sacred cedar post honoring a mythical hero said to have saved the tribe during a flood. They also built a large ceremonial lodge. Each village was led by a warrior chief and a civil leader. The Mandan were for the most part a peaceful tribe but defended themselves when necessary.

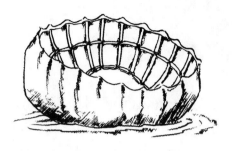

The Mandan were farmers and gatherers as well as hunters. The women cultivated the rich lands along the riverbanks, planting corn, squash, sunflower, and bean crops. As farmers they were prosperous. The women would load up the surplus crops into tub-shaped bullboats and paddle down-river to trade with other tribes. In addition to their farming chores, the women also made pottery, prepared the meals, carried water, and helped to build their earthen dwellings.

The men hunted deer, elk, porcupine, and beaver, but the buffalo was their main source of meat. Before acquiring guns and horses, the Mandan hunted on foot. The men would cover themselves in wolf skins and creep up on the grazing buffalo. They then used spears and bows and arrows to kill the animals and used a carrier made of two poles and a platform called a *travois* to carry the meat back to the village.

After the arrival of the Europeans, the Mandan became intermediaries between the newcomers and tribes to the west. Trading sessions were often held in Mandan villages, where shirts and robes made from buffalo hides were traded for goods such as cloth, knives, metal kettles, guns, and horses. Unfortunately, the Europeans also brought diseases with them, including smallpox. Hundreds and hundreds of Mandan and people from other tribes died during several epidemics.

# How the Mandan Came to Earth

In 1804 government explorers Meriwether Lewis and William Clark led an expedition through the northwestern territory. In October of that year, they reached one of five Mandan villages along the Missouri in what is now North Dakota. The explorers built a fort across the river and spent the winter there. The Mandan helped the newcomers. It was during this time that Lewis and Clark heard the legend about the origin of the Mandan tribe.

Long ago, before the time when people lived and farmed and hunted on earth, a tribe of people lived deep down below the surface. Their home was near a lake.

One day some of the underground people noticed the thirsty roots of a grapevine growing down toward the water in their lake. When they looked upward, they caught a glimpse of daylight. Curious, they decided to climb the grapevine to see where it would take them.

Natchitak, or Chief Above, and Atna, Mother Corn, led the people to the surface. One after another, the people followed, climbing the vine to the top. What they saw of the sun-drenched earth delighted them, for they found an abundance of buffalo, fruit, and everything they would need to thrive. When the others still below heard the news, they too decided to leave. And so, more and more men, women, and children came to the surface. Before long nearly half the group of underground people had reached the surface.

Then one day the grapevine broke under the weight and strain of all the people who were climbing it. Sadly, some of the Mandan were left behind where, it is said, they still remain.

Name _____ Date _____

# Designing a Mandan Shield

Mandan warriors used shields for protection. Shields were made from the thickest part of the buffalo's hide and then painted. Create a design for the shield below. Use your imagination and finish the design with markers or crayons.

© 1994 by Troll Associates.

# Playing Mandan Games

Most Native American tribes played a variety of games to sharpen their hunting and fighting skills. Young men of the Mandan tribes had contests to see who could shoot the most arrows into the air. First the archer shot an arrow in a high arc. Then he shot as many arrows as he could before the first arrow hit the ground. The winning archer got to keep the arrows of all the other players.

## Up and Away

Students can play a variation of this game using rubber balls instead of arrows. The student who can toss the most balls into the air before the first ball reaches the ground wins the round.

## Shooting Hoops

The Mandan also played a variation of hoop and pole, a game in which spears, arrows, or darts were thrown through moving netted hoops. The Mandan made smooth paths for their hoops. As a variation on this game, one student can move a hula hoop through the air as another student tries to toss balls through the hoop.

## Knee and Foot Ball

The Mandan played still another game, this one using a ball decorated with porcupine quills. To play, they dropped the ball alternately onto the foot and knee, tossing it up in the air each time. If the player missed, the ball was passed to the next player. Have students see how well they can keep a small soft ball in the air by alternately using their knee and foot.

# Using Sign Language

Many tribes of the Plains used signs and gestures to communicate with each other because they did not share a common language. Sometimes members of the same tribe used sign language if they were hunting prey or trying to surprise an enemy without being heard. Demonstrate these signs and have students practice them.

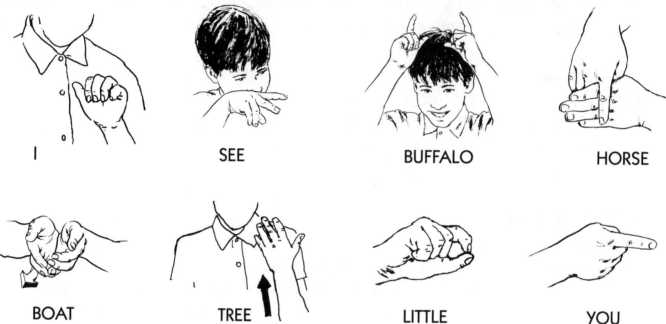

| I | SEE | BUFFALO | HORSE |
| BOAT | TREE | LITTLE | YOU |

Have students use some of the signs together to tell what they see.
For example:

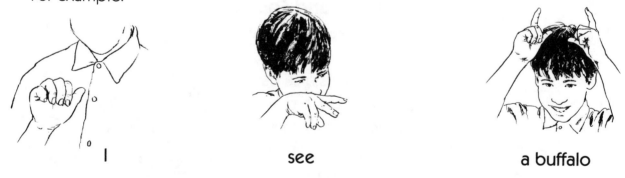

I      see      a buffalo

Then have students form groups to create their own signs for special messages. Have each group take turns signing their message for the class to guess.

# Making a Buffalo Mask

Buffalo were important to the Plains tribes. Many tribes performed buffalo-hunting dances to ensure a good hunt. When buffalo meat was running low in a Mandan village, men put on buffalo masks and performed the Buffalo Calling Dance to bring a herd to the grasslands. The dance could last for weeks until a herd was sighted. Have students make their own buffalo masks.

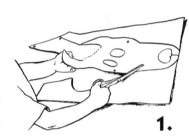

**1.**

### Materials:
approximately 11" x 28" (28 x 71 cm) rectangular sections of posterboard
scissors
hole punch
crayons, paints and paintbrushes, or markers
pieces of black or brown yarn
glue

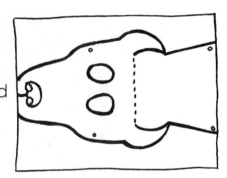

**1.**

**2.**

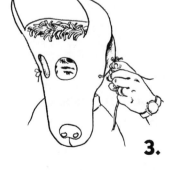

**3.**

### What students do:
**1.** Draw and cut out a posterboard pattern as shown. Cut out eyeholes and punch holes on the sides for string.

**2.** Use crayons, paints, or markers to decorate the buffalo head and horns. Glue yarn on top of mask for hair.

**3.** Tie the mask on with string.

Have students use their masks to create and perform their own Buffalo Calling Dance. They can use drums and rattles as background music for their dance. See pages 92 and 93.

# MEET THE
# BLACKFOOT

The Blackfoot migrated from the Northeast Woodlands to the foothills of the Rocky Mountains in the northwest corner of the Plains. Today this territory is known as the state of Montana. How the Blackfoot got their name is not known. However, according to one legend, their ancestors traveled across an area of prairie burned and blackened by fire. They walked for so many days in the ashes that their moccasins turned black.

The Blackfoot were one of the many Plains nomadic tribes who depended on the buffalo for survival. When they hunted buffalo during the summer, the Blackfoot had to be able to move about quickly and easily, carrying all their possessions with them. Toward this end, they lived in portable *tipis*, tent-like dwellings of buffalo skins stretched over a frame of wooden poles. When broken down, the ends of two poles were fastened to the shoulders of a dog or horse. The other ends dragged along the ground. A platform was laid across the poles to form a *travois*, a kind of sled. The remaining poles and the buffalo skins were then loaded onto the travois along with their other belongings.

The Blackfoot used several techniques to hunt buffalo. Sometimes the hunters drove the buffalo over a cliff. Other times they covered themselves with buffalo skins and horns to approach the animals without frightening them. The hunters then shot them with bows and arrows or spears. The acquisition of horses in the 1600s made tracking and hunting much more efficient and enabled the hunters to travel farther from camp.

The Blackfoot used every part of the buffalo. Once the buffalo had been killed, the women butchered them. Most of the meat was cut into strips and dried in the sun to make *jerky*. It was also pounded and mixed with berries and fat to make *pemmican*, a Blackfoot staple.

The fur on skins taken in late fall and winter was thick, so the women made the skins into robes and blankets. Skins taken in spring and summer were made into rawhide for clothing, hunting shields, tipi covers, rope for harnesses and bridles, and tools. The horns and bones were made into tools, utensils, ornaments, and needles. The hair was used to stuff pillows and cradleboards and to line moccasins. The "buffalo chips," or manure, were used for fuel.

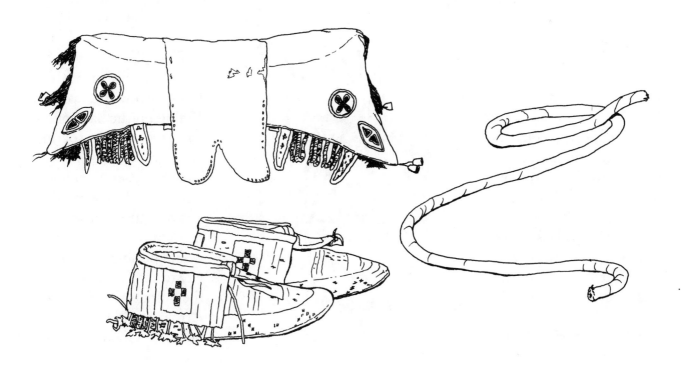

# How the Blackfoot Came to Have Horses

Life changed dramatically for the Blackfoot and other tribes after they acquired horses from Spanish explorers in the early 1600s. This Blackfoot legend tells how their people came to have horses.

It was told that the spirit people who lived at the bottom of a great faraway lake had a herd of mysterious animals that were bigger than the great elk but carried their loads like the travois dogs. The animal was known as *Pono-Kamita*, or Elk Dog.

From time to time, young warriors had set out to find the Elk Dogs, but none had ever come back. Long Arrow, an orphan adopted by Chief Good Running, decided he would try.

When the time was right, Long Arrow headed south to find the lake. After many days, Long Arrow reached a body of water. There he was greeted by a frightful spirit man, twice his size. "Why have you come here?" the man demanded.

Long Arrow said without fear, "I have come to find Elk Dogs."

"I cannot help you," the man said, "but perhaps my grandfather will. You must walk south until you reach a great lake."

After many days, Long Arrow reached the great lake. Tired and hungry, he was greeted by a spirit boy.

"We have been expecting you," the boy said. "My

grandfather waits for you below. Follow me."

At that, the boy changed into a kingfisher bird and dove into the lake. Fearing that he might drown but knowing that he must follow, Long Arrow bravely jumped into the water. To his amazement, the water parted before him, and he could breathe and see.

At the lake bottom, Long Arrow came to the lodge of a black robed old man, the Great One. Together they feasted. When Long Arrow had satisfied his hunger, the spirit chief spoke: "All the others before you were afraid of deep water. They left with nothing. Your bravery shows that you are the chosen one. You will receive the gift you seek to bring your people."

The Elk Dogs were the most beautiful animals Long Arrow had ever seen. Riding on the back of an Elk Dog was like soaring through the air as a bird. They were stronger and swifter, and they could carry ten times more than a dog. Soon his people would be able to go anywhere they wanted to hunt the buffalo. And Long Arrow would bring great honor to Good Running.

# Living in a Tipi

There wasn't a lot of living space in a tipi.  Show students the picture of the tipi. Have students make a floor plan of a tipi.

## Materials:
40-60 foot (12-18 m) length of
    yarn or rope
index cards
chalk

## What students do:
**1.** Clear a large circular space in the class-room and mark if off with yarn or rope.

**2.** Write down on the index cards or on the chalkboard what would be needed to live inside the tipi for several months without electricity, plumbing, or any heat source other than a fire.

**3.** Estimate how much space the necessities would occupy.

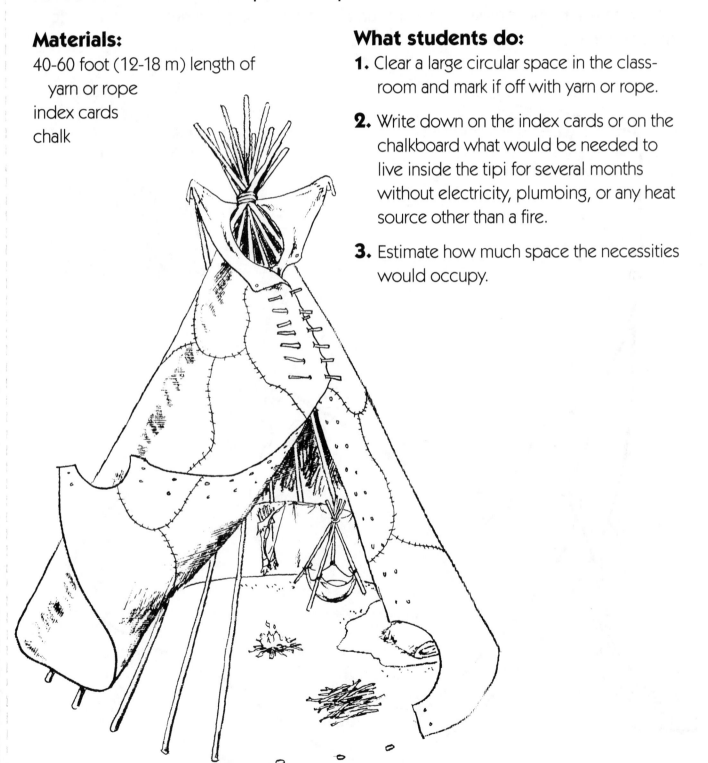

Name  Date

# Designing a Parfleche

The Blackfoot made rawhide carryalls, or *parfleches*, to hold food, clothing, and other items. Traditionally, the women painted geometric designs on parfleches. Decorate the parfleche below by creating a design, using a variety of geometric shapes and colors.

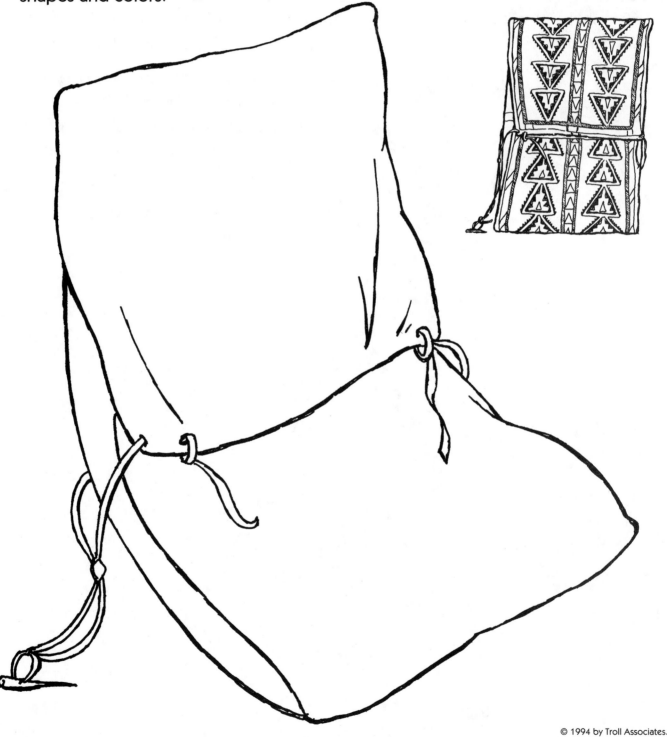

© 1994 by Troll Associates.

# Making a "Buffalo Skin" Picture Autobiography

People of the Plains sometimes used the hide of a buffalo like an artist's canvas to record important events in a person's life. Show students the picture of the hide, which depicts the life of a Plains warrior. Have students make their own "buffalo hide" picture autobiography to record the important events in their lives.

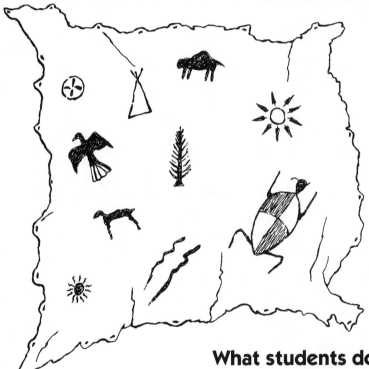

## Materials:

scissors

paints, paintbrushes, and markers

a large sheet of brown wrapping paper
for each student (A brown grocery bag
that has been cut open will also work.)

## Teacher:

Help students copy a shape like the one above onto their papers and then cut them out to make "buffalo hides."

## What students do:

1. List important events in their lives, such as the day they were born, their first step or word, the first day of school, etc.

2. Design symbols to depict these milestones.

3. Paint or use markers to create the symbols on the "buffalo hide."

Display the picture "autobiographies" and have the artists tell about them.

Name _____ Date _____

# How the Blackfoot Came to Have Dogs

A Blackfoot legend tells of Long Arrow, a boy whose bravery earns him the gift of the horse to bring back to his people.  Yet before the Blackfoot had horses, they used travois dogs to carry heavy loads as they traveled from place to place.  Write a story of your own about how these faithful dogs came to help the Blackfoot. You can use the back of this page to continue your story.

_____

_____

_____

_____

_____

_____

_____

© 1994 by Troll Associates.

Name _____ Date _____

# A Vision Quest

Imagine you are a Blackfoot youth alone in the wilderness. You've spent three days and nights without food. You're praying for a vision of an animal like the wolf so you can capture its spirit and acquire its strength. Close your eyes. What do you see? Record your impressions in a drawing or a piece of writing.

© 1994 by Troll Associates.

# THE LAND AND PEOPLE OF THE
# SOUTHWEST

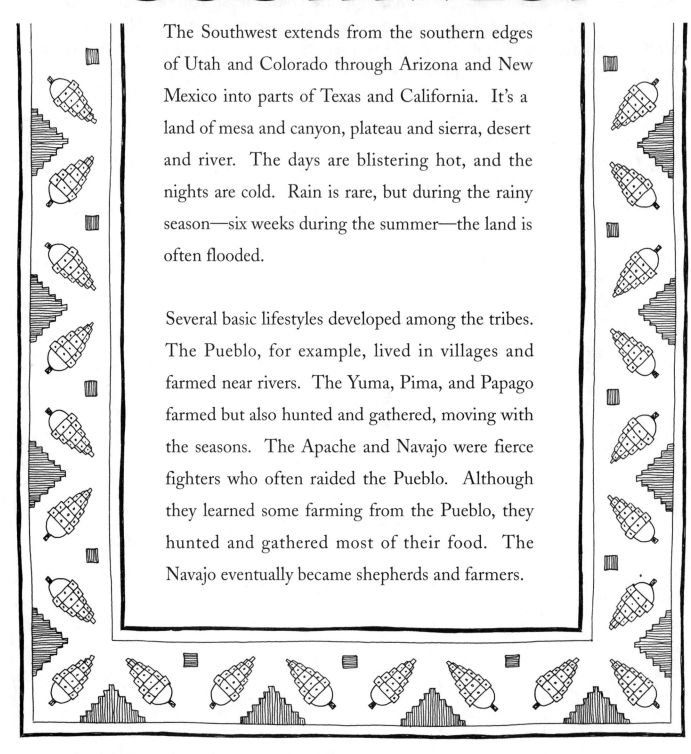

The Southwest extends from the southern edges of Utah and Colorado through Arizona and New Mexico into parts of Texas and California. It's a land of mesa and canyon, plateau and sierra, desert and river. The days are blistering hot, and the nights are cold. Rain is rare, but during the rainy season—six weeks during the summer—the land is often flooded.

Several basic lifestyles developed among the tribes. The Pueblo, for example, lived in villages and farmed near rivers. The Yuma, Pima, and Papago farmed but also hunted and gathered, moving with the seasons. The Apache and Navajo were fierce fighters who often raided the Pueblo. Although they learned some farming from the Pueblo, they hunted and gathered most of their food. The Navajo eventually became shepherds and farmers.

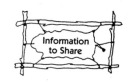

# MEET THE PUEBLO

**W**hen the Spaniards arrived in the Southwest, they encountered large villages of multi-storied dwellings built from stone and adobe. Some of the villages were built along the sides of cliffs. Others were built atop mesas. The Spaniards called this type of village a *pueblo*, the Spanish word for "village." The villages resembled apartment buildings. The stone and clay or adobe dwellings had as many as four stories. Reaching the upper levels required climbing a ladder.

The people who lived in the villages came to be called the Pueblo, but not all came from the same tribe. The Pueblo include the Hopi in Arizona, the Zuñi, Laguna, and Acoma in New Mexico, and the Kere, Tewa, Towa, and Tiwa of the Rio Grande. Their languages and cultures differed somewhat, but they shared similar spiritual beliefs.

The Pueblo believed that the earth provided them with all they needed to live, and that everything—plants, animals, people, rocks, rain, and wind—had a spirit. According to legend and to Sipapu, the Great Spirit, the people were responsible for caring for the earth, protecting it, and maintaining its balance. The Pueblo honored the spirit world with ceremonies and rites, some of which were held in *kivas*, underground rooms.

The Pueblo also shared a common ancestor, the Anasazi, or "ancient ones." They inhabited the area where Arizona, Colorado, New Mexico, and Utah now meet. Though at first hunters and gatherers, the Anasazi eventually learned to cultivate crops and settled down. Over the centuries, their dwellings evolved from pit houses into huge, complex, semicircular apartment compounds of stone and adobe. One such village was Pueblo Bonito in New Mexico.

A combination of problems caused the Anasazi to abandon this settlement and others like it. Perhaps the biggest problem was a drought between 1276 and 1299. Then and later, many people moved and settled elsewhere, some along the Rio Grande River and others along the Little Colorado River where they established new pueblos. This is where the Spaniards came as they made their way north from Mexico in the 1500s.

# The Daily Life of a Pueblo Girl

Morning Star lives in a large canyon village. She shares a one-room house with her parents, brothers, and grandmother. Morning Star's aunt, uncle, and cousins live in a house that is attached to theirs.

To reach the houses, Morning Star and her family must climb a ladder. A low doorway opens into their house, which is dark because there are no windows. This helps to keep out the heat of the sun during the day. Shelves built into the wall hold some of their belongings. Morning Star's sheepskin sleeping rug is in the corner next to the other rugs and blankets her father has woven. When it is time to eat everyone will use the rolled up blankets to sit on the floor.

Down the street, a family is adding a room onto a house. The men have already brought the stones and the beams for the roof. As they set the stones in place, the women fill in the spaces with mud. Inside, the women will plaster the walls. Then they will put grass and brush over the beams of the roof and add a final coat of mud. The stone and adobe walls absorb the heat, helping to keep the house cool during the day and warm at night.

During spring, the men in the village plant corn, using irrigation ditches to bring water to the growing crops. Each summer the village holds a special festival that marks the return of the spirits called *kachinas* to their mythical home. On the last day, kachina dancers perform a special dance to bring the rain clouds.

When autumn arrives, the men will harvest the crops. The Pueblo will eat some of the corn, save some for seed, and store the rest. One of Morning Star's tasks is to braid the corn by the husks and hang them to dry. She is also learning to grind the corn into meal and to make *piki*, a cake made from cornmeal, water, and wood ash batter which she will cook on a special stone slab called a *duma*. Morning Star will also learn to weave baskets and make pottery.

# Making a Kachina Doll

The Pueblo believed the Kachina spirits would bring them good health, happiness, and abundant harvests. Many ceremonies honored the Kachinas. Dancers wearing kilts and elaborate masks to look like the Kachinas led the celebrations. Children were also given Kachina dolls. Show students the picture of the dolls. Then have them make their own Kachinas.

## Materials:

cardboard tubes of differing sizes,
   some cut in short sections for use as
   headpieces or arms and legs,
   or clean quart or liter-sized milk cartons
paints and paintbrushes
construction paper scraps
scissors
fabric scraps, beads, buttons, feathers
glue
assorted markers

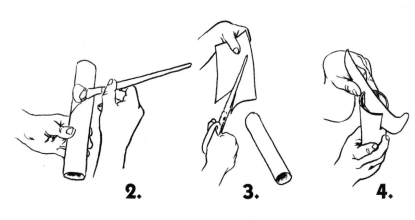

**2.**     **3.**     **4.**

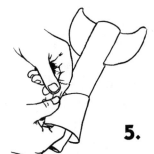

**5.**

## What students do:

**1.** Choose a spirit for the doll to represent, such as a bird or other animal, or the sun and clouds.

**2.** Have each student paint a large-sized cardboard tube or milk carton white and let it dry.

**3.** Make a separate headdress out of construction paper.

**4.** Cut slits on opposite sides at the top and slide the headdress in place.

**5.** Use fabric scraps, cardboard tubes, paper scraps, markers, paints, beads, buttons, and feathers to make the features for the head and body.

Name _____ Date _____

# Making Pueblo Pottery Designs

The Pueblo people made beautiful pottery. Typically they painted black designs on a bright, white background. Following the Pueblo style, add designs to the undecorated pieces of pottery in the picture with a black marker.

© 1994 by Troll Associates.

# Grinding Corn the Native American Way

Pueblo boys and girls learned many different skills at an early age. Boys learned to hunt, farm, and weave. Girls were taught to care for younger children, prepare foods, weave baskets, and make pottery. Grinding corn was another skill that all Pueblo girls learned.

Using a stone called a *mano*, they mashed dried corn kernels against a stone slab called a *metate*. They used three metates of different textures so that they could grind the corn into the finest meal possible. Show students the picture of the woman grinding corn. Invite students to grind corn in the Native American way.

## Materials:

a wooden bowl to serve as a *metate*
a hard rock with smooth rounded edges
   to serve as a *mano*
plenty of dried corn kernels

## What students do:

**1.** Have students put a handful of corn kernels in the bowl.

**2.** Take turns using the rock to gently pound, mash, and grind the corn into meal.

**3.** After everyone has had an opportunity to grind corn, sprinkle the meal in a location where it can be eaten by the birds.

# MEET THE NAVAJO

L ate in the 1400s, the Navajo came to what is now northwestern New Mexico and northeastern Arizona. They called this land of peaks, grasslands, deserts, and canyons *Dinetkah*, "Home of the People."

Ancestors of the Navajo had migrated from Canada. They were hunters and trappers, making simple shelters as they moved about. Their nomadic way of life gradually changed as they came in contact with the Pueblo tribes already living in the region. In fact, the Pueblo gave the new people the name of Navajo, which means "takers from the field," because of their practice of raiding the Pueblo and stealing crops, tools, looms, pottery, blankets, and anything else they could use.

In the years that followed, the Navajo also adopted some of the beliefs, customs, and practices of the Pueblo. They continued to hunt, but they also learned to farm, make pottery, and weave, a skill that would make them world famous.

As the Navajo turned to farming, they began to build more permanent settlements, small clusters of homes called *hogans*. At first the Navajo built their hogans out of timbers and poles covered with dirt and bark. Later, this gave way to a six-sided hogan built of logs and mud.

When the Spaniards came to the area, they brought with them sheep, cattle, and horses. The Navajo and other tribes raided the new settlers, but instead of killing and eating all the sheep, they began to build up the herds for themselves. The animals would eventually provide them with a steady supply of meat for food and wool for weaving.

As in many other Native American cultures, women were the homeowners, not the men. When a Navajo man married, he moved into his wife's home. If the couple had a daughter, she would inherit the hogan, her mother's goods, and the sheep. Even after marriage, a man was still responsible to his mother's clan, particularly to his sisters and their children, for one day they would be his heirs, not his own children.

The Navajo were greatly influenced by their belief in supernatural beings known as the Holy People. Should a Navajo ignore or break any of the hundreds of ancient rules, the spirits could show their anger and displeasure by causing illness, bad luck, disaster, sorrow, and death. As a consequence, the Navajo worked hard to live in harmony with the universe and the spirits.

# The Daily Life of a Navajo Boy

Running Horse is a Navajo boy who lives with his parents and three younger sisters in a *hogan*. The frame is made of logs and sticks, covered with mud and bark. His grandmother and an unmarried aunt live in a hogan nearby. When his aunt marries, she and her husband will build a new hogan. Running Horse's father is away now. He is helping his sister and her children, as is the Navajo custom.

As the sun begins to rise, Running Horse's mother is sprinkling corn pollen on the hogan to honor the spirits they call the Holy People. Running Horse's sisters are stirring, but the baby is still asleep in the cradleboard. When everyone is awake, Running Horse's mother will clean the hogan.

Running Horse goes outside to the sheep corral. On the way he passes by the family's garden. This year the corn, squash, and bean plants are growing well. His mother will pick some of the vegetables for their meal. Running Horse especially likes mutton with corn and squash and the fry bread his mother often prepares.

When Running Horse reaches the corral, he lets the sheep out and drives them to the pasture. He likes to tend the sheep, especially the new lambs. Later in the day, he will drive them back to the corral where they will stay until the next morning. Today Running Horse must also collect wood for the fire.

While Running Horse tends the sheep, his mother, sisters, aunt, and grandmother work with the wool. They must wash and dye it before they can use it to weave the blankets and rugs. The women use roots, weeds, and flowers to make the dyes.

At the end of the day, the family gathers for a meal. Running Horse helps his sisters spread the sheepskin on the ground for the bowls. Before long, they are sitting on the ground around the bowls and dipping into the delicious smelling foods.

As night falls, Running Horse, his sisters, and their mother return to the hogan. They spread the sheepskins around the fire pit once again and lie down, clothes and all, with their feet toward the fire. Soon everyone is asleep for the night.

Name _____  Date _____

# Making a Navajo Blanket Design

The Navajo are skilled weavers.  A rug woven by the women covers the doorway to this hogan.  You can design a blanket on the loom below.  Use stripes and bands, diamond shapes, crosses, zigzags, and angles.

© 1994 by Troll Associates.

# Weaving

The Navajo used looms to weave their blankets. Show students the picture of these blankets. Then have them use simple weaving techniques to make wall hangings.

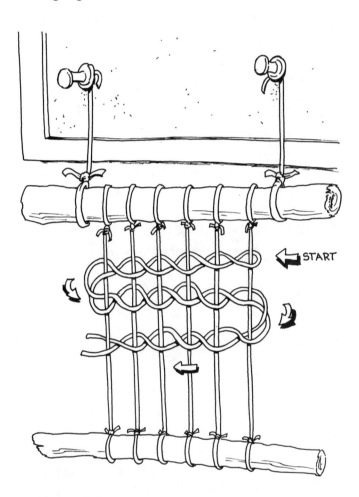

## Materials:

2 wood dowels or sturdy tree branches
different-colored yarn
twine or heavy string
pushpins
scissors

## What students do:

**1.** Cut two lengths of twine and tie one end to each end of one of the dowels or branches. Attach the other ends to a bulletin board with pushpins.

**2.** Cut twine into equal lengths. Tie each to the branch at intervals of 1/2 inch (1.27cm) to make a weaving frame.

**3.** Tie the ends of the twine to another branch at the bottom.

**4.** Alternately weave different-colored yarns and twine over and under the strings to create a design.

Demonstrate some of these techniques for students to try.

# Making a Dry Painting

As a part of a healing ceremony for sick or injured tribe members, the Navajo used colored sands, crushed charcoal, cornmeal, mineral ores, and pollen to create elaborate dry paintings on a bed of sand. After the ceremony, the painting was swept away. Show students the picture. Then have them create their own paintings.

## Materials:

sand
paper cups
food coloring
fork
cardboard sheets
pencils
newspaper
glue

## What Students do:

**1.** Make colored sand by adding several drops of food coloring to cups of sand. Mix thoroughly with a fork.

**2.** While the sand dries, make a pencil sketch of a design on the cardboard.

**3.** Place the cardboard on newspaper. Then apply a thin layer of glue over the penciled areas.

**4.** Sprinkle the sand over the areas of wet glue one color at a time.

**5.** Lift the cardboard to one side so the extra sand will fall onto the newspaper.

**6.** Let the painting dry.

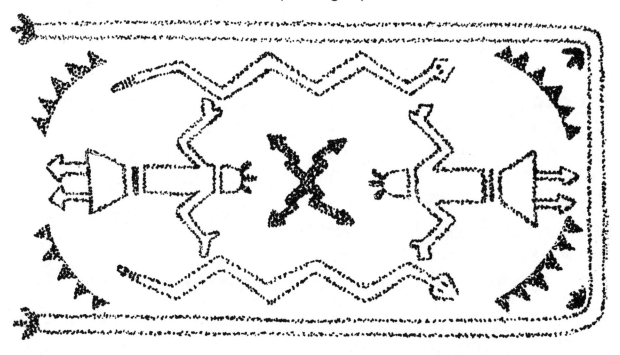

# Making Fry Bread

The Navajo ate fry bread made from wheat flour. Make fry bread with your students. This recipe makes about 12-14 servings. Adjust the ingredients according to the number of students.

## Materials:

4 cups (1 liter) flour
1 tablespoon (15 ml) baking powder
1 1/2 teaspoon (7 ml) salt
1 1/2 teaspoon (7 ml) cooking oil
warm water
1/2 inch (1 cm) of hot shortening

electric frying pan
tongs or spatula
bowl
clean damp dish towel
paper towels

## What students do:

1. Mix together the flour, salt, and baking powder.

2. Add the oil and some water to make a soft dough.

3. Knead the dough until it is springy. It should not be sticky. Let rise in a bowl covered with a clean, damp dish towel for 2 hours.

4. Shape the dough into small balls about 2 to 3 inches (about 5 to 8 cm) across.

5. Flatten the balls until they are about 10 inches (about 25 cm) across.

6. Fry the dough in about 1/2 inch (about 1 cm) of hot shortening. Use tongs to turn and remove the bread from the frying pan. It should be puffy and golden brown.

7. Drain the fry bread on paper towels.

# THE LAND AND PEOPLE OF THE NORTHWEST COAST

The Northwest Coast is a long, narrow strip of land that stretches from the Alaska panhandle to northern California. A rugged chain of wooded mountains runs the length of the coast. Numerous rivers fed by melting snow and ice flow to the sea. The oceans, rivers, and forests provided the Tlingit, Chinook, Kwakiutl, and others all they needed to live. The people fished for salmon, halibut, cod, and other fish. They gathered clams, mussels, berries, plants, and seaweed, and collected the eggs of shore birds. They hunted whales, seals, and other sea mammals, and deer, elk, goats, bears, and small game from the forests. Trees provided wood for dwellings, canoes, weapons, utensils, tools, pipes, and masks. Bark and roots were used for weaving. They grew tobacco but otherwise did not farm.

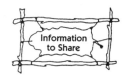
# MEET THE
# TLINGIT

**T**he Tlingit inhabited southern Alaska. Like other Northwest Coast tribes, the Tlingit lived in villages along the shore. Every structure—houses, smokehouses, drying racks, storage sheds, and huts for special ceremonies and rites—was made of wood. Related families lived in huge cedar plank houses which had a hole in the roof with a sliding panel. If a household member was of high rank, a carved totem pole stood in front.

The Tlingit were divided into two major groups, Eagles and Ravens. Each group was further divided into smaller clans. The men in any household belonged to the same clan; children were considered part of their mothers' clans. As in other Native American cultures, a man's children did not inherit his wealth; his sister's children did.

Fishing was a main source of Tlingit food and wealth. The late spring was especially important. Men and women gathered along freshwater streams to catch salmon as they swam upstream to spawn. Also during the spring, the Tlingit fished for herring and eulachon, used for its oil. In winter, fishermen went out into the ocean in dugout canoes to fish for halibut and cod.

Rank was important to the Tlingit. It was determined by family background and a person's wealth. Although obtaining wealth was important, sharing it was important, too. This was evident during the ceremony called the *potlatch*. This huge feast was given by the house of one clan to show and share one's wealth. Several hundred guests were invited for ten days or more, and the host was responsible for providing food and housing for all of the guests. Huge amounts of fish, seafood, meat, seaweed, berries, and fish oil were prepared and served in enormous serving dishes. To honor their host, guests were expected to eat as much as they possibly could.

The Tlingit traded their own goods with the Eskimo to the north and with tribes to the east, but they were also the trading middlemen for tribes to the north, south, and east. They would receive goods from the south, for example, keep some, and trade the rest to eastern tribes for copper and caribou skins.

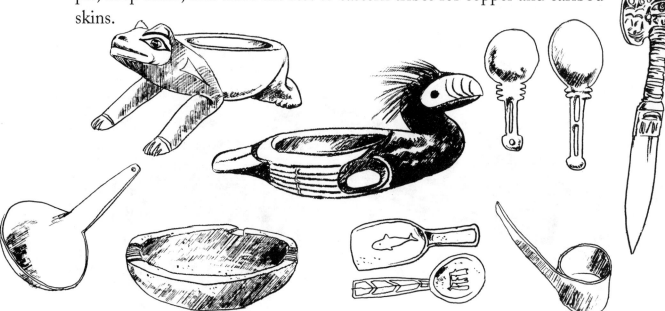

# Carving a Totem Pole

In villages along the Northwest coast, skilled carvers created totem poles from the trunks of cedar trees.  A pole could represent a clan, illustrate its mythological history, or honor the dead.  Show students the pictures of the totem poles.  Then have them carve their own miniature totem poles.

## Materials:

drawing paper
pencils
modeling clay
plastic knives

## What students do:

**1.** Sketch a totem pole design on drawing paper.

**2.** Carve the clay with the plastic knives.

**3.** Use extra pieces of clay for features such as wings, beaks, or ears, and press the pieces in place.

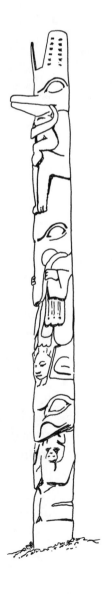

# The Story of the Raven and the Tides

Tribes of the Northwest Coast depended on the sea for much of their food. The Tsimshian tribe tells the story of how low tide was created so the people could gather clams, crabs, seaweed, and other foods from the beaches.

Long ago, people along the coast often went hungry. They were unable to gather clams, crabs, mussels, seaweed, and all the other good things to eat because these things were hidden in the deep waters just off shore. For much of the time, the ocean was high, and the tide could neither come in nor go out.

Raven knew that something had to change, so he set out to see what he could do. He followed the line of tide as he flew high above the coast. After a while, he saw an old woman holding the tide line in her hand. Raven knew that unless she let go, the tide would stay high.

Raven landed in front of the old woman's house. "Old woman," he began, "I have just eaten some clams and they were delicious."

Curious, the old woman asked, "What clams?"

Raven patted his belly, saying, "I picked as many clams as I could eat along the shore, and now I am very full."

"That's not possible!" said the old woman.

She walked to the doorway and leaned over to get a better look at Raven. With that, Raven gave her a push. As she fell to the ground, Raven tossed dust into her eyes so she would not be able to see.

The old woman dropped the tide line. Suddenly, the tide flowed back to reveal clams, crabs, mussels, seaweed, and all the other good things to eat.

Raven went down to the beach to gather clams. Before long others had come to gather the food, too. They were grateful to Raven.

After he had eaten his fill, Raven returned to the old woman's house. Although she could not see, she knew that Raven was there. She asked him to heal her eyes.

Raven said, "If you promise to release the tide line two times each day, I will heal your eyes."

When the old woman agreed, Raven rinsed out her eyes so she could see once more.

To this day, the tide comes in and goes out twice a day. The people are able to gather clams, crabs, mussels, seaweed, and all the other good foods the ocean provides.

Name _____   Date _____

# Writing a Tlingit Tale

Many Tlingit tales tell about Raven, the clever trickster.  In one, Raven is a white bird who steals the sun from a box belonging to his uncle, Nascakiyel, creator of the world.  Make up your own story in which you tell how Raven got into his uncle's plank house, how he escaped, and how he came to be black like soot instead of white.  Use the other side of this page to continue your story.

Long ago, when the world was without light,

_____

_____

_____

_____

_____

_____

_____

_____

_____

_____

© 1994 by Troll Associates.

# THE LAND AND PEOPLE OF THE
# SUBARCTIC AND ARCTIC

The Subarctic was home to tribes such as the Koyukon, Chilcotin, Yellowknife, Chipewyan, Swampy Cree, and Beothuk. The region covers nearly all of Canada and much of the Alaska interior. The southern Subarctic is a land of forests, lakes, and rivers. To the northwest are mountains and a vast treeless area called the *tundra*. The tribes coped with long, bitterly cold, snow-filled winters and short summers with swarms of mosquitoes and black flies. Most tribes were nomadic and hunted, fished, and foraged for food. Life for many was tied to the seasonal migrations of the caribou.

North of the Subarctic region is a treeless land called the Arctic. It stretches from eastern Siberia to Greenland. Winters are long and extremely harsh with few hours of sunlight. Gale force winds fuel intense blizzards and create huge drifts. The Inuit and Aleut, tribes who adapted to the harsh Arctic, hunted sea mammals and caribou. What they did not eat, they used for clothing, shelter, boats, dog sleds, tools, and weapons.

# MEET THE
# CHIPEWYAN

**A**ncestors of the Subarctic tribe known as the Chipewyan probably crossed the Bering land bridge from Asia around 12,000 years ago. The Chipewyan eventually came to inhabit an area where the forest gave way to *tundra*, a vast treeless area, in what is now Canada.

Caribou and moose were the main sources of food, clothing, and shelter for the Chipewyan. Each spring, the caribou migrated hundreds of miles from the forest to the tundra in herds numbering 100,000. The nomadic Chipewyan families followed the herds during these seasonal migrations.

The Chipewyan also caught and ate fish such as trout, whitefish, and pike from the lakes and rivers of the region. To catch the fish, the men used nets, weirs, and barbed arrows and spears. The fish were usually dried and smoked for the winter. There were few plants in the Chipewyan diet, but they were known to eat moss.

In winter when the Chipewyan returned from the tundra to the forests, food stores of dried fish and meat often dwindled, and the people faced starvation. Although the men hunted rabbit and hibernating bears and tracked moose or caribou, game was hard to find in the snow-covered, bitter cold north woods.

The Chipewyan lived in portable dwellings similar to the tipi of the Plains tribes. They made a circular framework of poles, which they tied loosely at the top. Then they covered the framework with as many as 70 caribou skins sewn together, leaving a smoke hole at the top and covering the floor with branches.

Although hunting was the primary job of Chipewyan men, women were responsible for nearly everything else. They hauled water and made the fires. They skinned, butchered, and prepared the caribou. Using primitive tools, the women processed the hides and made them into clothes, covers for the tipis, and blankets. Women and children pulled the toboggans and carried the heavy loads when the tribe migrated. As the women and children moved the camp, the men hunted for game in the surrounding woods. Life was a constant struggle for these people who followed the caribou.

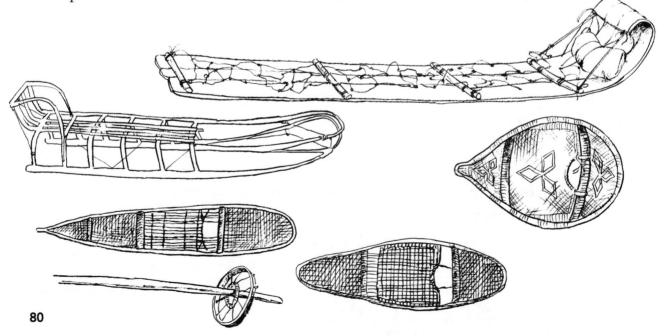

Name _____ Date _____

# Creating a Birch Bark Design

Subarctic women made beautiful symmetrical designs by biting into folded sheets of birch bark with their canine teeth. A design has been started. Can you finish it? Use short pencil strokes to make "teeth" marks. The design should be symmetrical when you finish.

© 1994 by Troll Associates.

# Making a Rock Painting

Throughout the Subarctic, people painted animals and supernatural figures called *Manitous* on rocks. Show students the picture of the rock painting. Help students make their own rock paintings.

## Materials:

drawing paper and pencils
clean, dry rocks (Students may want to
   bring in their own rocks.)
paintbrushes
tempera paints
newspaper to cover desks

## What students do:

**1.** Choose a rock.

**2.** With the class, brainstorm a list of birds, mammals, reptiles, and amphibians that live in the region.

**3.** Choose an animal from the list and sketch an abstract design to represent it.

**4.** Cover the desk with newspaper. Paint the design on the rock.

**5.** Invite classmates to identify the animal in the design.

# Writing and Illustrating a Class Story

Some Subarctic tribes believed that Windigos—giant, evil spirits—roamed the forests. People believed that these hissing, howling giants with clawlike hands, huge pointed teeth, and bloody-looking eyes, were made of ice. Students will enjoy creating their own pictures and stories of Windigo monsters.

Organize your class into an art group and a writing group. Provide them with the following materials and directions.

## Materials:

white freezer paper to cover a
  bulletin board
pencils
poster paints

flashlights
posterboard in various sizes
scissors
writing materials

## What students do:

**1.** Students in the art group line a bulletin board with white freezer paper, then sketch and paint a forest background. Each student draws and cuts out a posterboard Windigo shape before painting and placing it on the forest mural.

**2.** Writing students brainstorm ideas for the plot of Windigo tales that begin with these lines:

*Far in the North, where the winds howl without stopping, where the night lasts nearly all day . . .*

*Neither the hoods of their warm jackets or their earmuffs could block out the unending screams the campers heard as they tried to sleep.*

*Whoosh! Whoosh! Whoosh! The nearly frozen boy and girl pushed their snowshoes through the black forest of towering trees.*

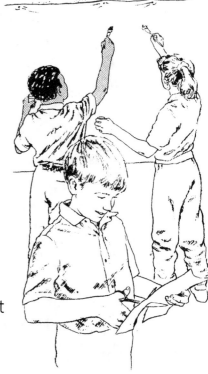

**3.** After students work cooperatively to brainstorm their story plots, they should work in pairs to develop and write several Windigo stories.

When the mural is dry and the Windigo stories are finished, set aside time for storytelling. Darken the room and flash a light on the mural as students read their stories while standing in front of the display.

# MEET THE ALEUT

The Aleutians, a chain of many treeless islands stretching west from the southern tip of Alaska, separate the Bering Sea to the north from the Pacific Ocean to the south. The islands are mostly mountainous with some active volcanoes. The weather changes suddenly and is said to be the worst in the world—wind, dense fog and mist, rain, and snow. Yet, for several thousand years, the Aleut have called these islands their home.

The Aleut share many characteristics with the Eskimo, or Inuit, including some physical traits. In addition, their languages are similar, and both once depended on the sea for food. They hunted seal, sea lions, whales, sea otters. The Aleut also hunted birds, trapped fish and shellfish, and gathered berries and roots. Like the Inuit, the Aleut also used stone lamps fueled with whale or seal oil for light and heat, and both hunted from kayaks.

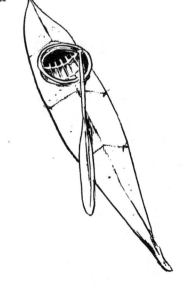

The Aleut used the fur, skin, sinew, and bones of the animals they hunted to make their clothing, dwellings, boats, weapons, and tools. They even used seal intestines to make waterproof parkas and bird skins to make skirts. Some Aleut made and wore fur stockings and leather boots. They also made wooden hats to protect their eyes from the glare of the sea.

The Aleut were skilled weavers and used certain grasses to make a fine silk-like thread, which they used to weave baskets. The baskets had very delicate patterns with as many as forty stitches to the inch (2.54 cm).

The Aleut lived in villages along the shore. To protect themselves from the weather, they built large underground communal houses called *barabaras*. The roof was made of driftwood and whalebone with a covering of sod. These houses could be quite large—240 feet (about 73 m) long and 40 feet (about 12 m) wide. Such a house might shelter many families.

The Aleut had a social class system that included slaves. Each island group had its own chief, or *toyon*, a person of wealth and high status who, with local nobles, ruled over the commoners and slaves. Signs of wealth were a man's possessions—slaves, amber, decorated clothing, and *dentalium*, or tooth shells.

Life for the Aleut changed forever with the coming of Russian sea otter traders in the 1740s. In the years that followed, sea otter, seal, and fox populations were nearly wiped out. Many Aleut were taken as slaves by Russians because of their hunting and fishing skills. In 1867 the Russians sold Alaska and the Aleutian Islands to the United States.

# Making an Aleut Hat

Aleut nobles wore hats made of thin board. First they steamed the wood. Next, they bent it and sewed it up in the back. Then they painted and decorated the hats with beads and sea lion whiskers. Show students the picture of an Aleut hat. Then have them make their own versions.

## Materials:

scissors
large sheets of thin cardboard or oaktag
cardboard and oaktag scraps
assorted markers or crayons
tape and glue
tall dried weeds or grasses for sea lion whiskers

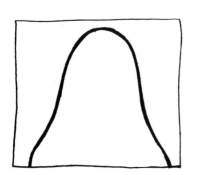

**1.**

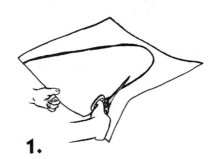

**2.**

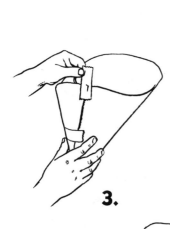

**3.**

**4.**

## What Students do:

**1.** Draw the outline shown and use the scissors to cut it out.

**2.** Use markers or crayons to create a design.

**3.** Overlap the opposite corners of the cardboard and tape up the back to make a seam.

**4.** Make decorations from cardboard or oaktag scraps and glue them to the sides of the hat. Glue dried grass or weeds for sea lion whiskers.

# Making an Animal Soap Carving

Arctic tribes used ivory, bone, wood, and soapstone to make sculptures of the animals in their environment, such as the polar bear, seal, walrus, whale, owl, and caribou. Such sculptures were usually smooth and rounded without a great many fine details. Show students the pictures of the animal carvings. Then have them make their own.

## Materials for each student:
a bar of soap
a paper clip
a plastic knife
pencil
a sheet of newspaper

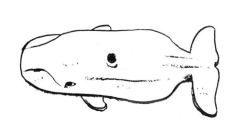

## What students do:
**1.** Choose an Arctic animal to carve.

**2.** Sketch the outline of the animal onto the bar of soap with a pencil. Keep the sketch very simple as the Aleut did.

**3.** Work over a newspaper-covered desk to carve off large pieces of soap from the sculpture. Use the end of the paper clip to carve small details.

Display the completed sculptures for everyone to enjoy.

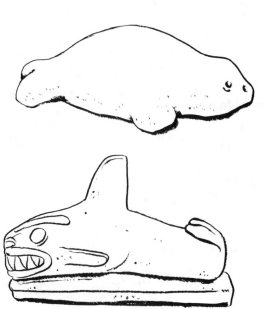

Answers for p. 88: 1-60 ft. (about 18 m);
2-45 ft. (about 13.7 m); 3-30 ft. (about 9.1 m);
4-15 ft. (about 4.6 m); 5-25 ft. (about 7.6 m);
6-30 ft. (about 9.1 m)

# Comparing Whales and the Umiak

Arctic tribes hunted whales in a boat called the *umiak*. Use the following information to complete the chart and find out how long the umiak was.

The bowhead whale is 60 feet (18 m) long. The gray whale is about 3/4 the length of the bowhead whale. The killer whale is 1/2 the length of the bowhead whale. The beluga whale is about 1/4 the length of the bowhead whale. From tusk to tail, the narwhal is 5/6 the length of the killer whale. The umiak boat is the same length as a killer whale. How long is the umiak boat?

**1.** Bowhead whale   =   60 feet (18 m)
**2.** Gray whale   =   _____
**3.** Killer whale   =   _____
**4.** Beluga whale   =   _____
**5.** Narwhal   =   _____
**6.** Umiak boat   =   _____

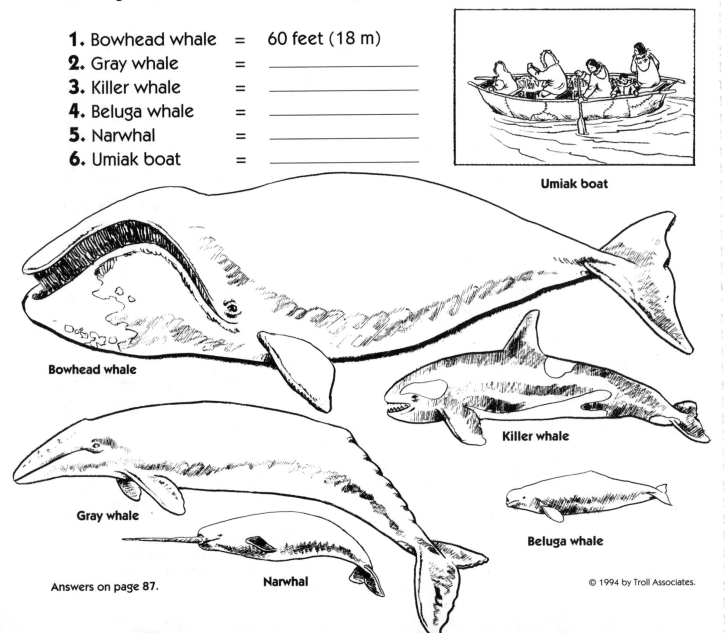

**Umiak boat**

**Bowhead whale**

**Killer whale**

**Gray whale**

**Beluga whale**

**Narwhal**

Answers on page 87.

© 1994 by Troll Associates.

# Playing Arctic Games

People of the Arctic enjoyed playing a variety of games. Share them with your students. Then have them create their own variations.

## Airborne Animals

The Inuit played a game similar to dice with small carved animal and bird figures, which they tossed on the ground. The object was to get the figures to land upright or to face the challenger.

## Spinning Target

In *nugluktaq*, players tried to be the first to poke a stick through the hole in a piece of spinning bone suspended from above.

## Inuit Kickball

The object of Inuit kickball was to keep the other team from getting control of the ball. The ball was leather stuffed with caribou hair and was only about 5 inches (about 13 cm) across.

## Arctic Catch

Four players standing in a square were needed for the Arctic toss and catch. Players batted the ball with their palms open to the teammate in the opposite corner.

## Pull Away

For *arsuruniq* a strip of sinew was tied to the middle of two pieces of antler. Players sat opposite each other on the ground, legs out straight and feet touching. Each person held the antler in one hand and pulled backwards without bending the arm or legs. The person who was pulled over or who dropped the antler lost the round.

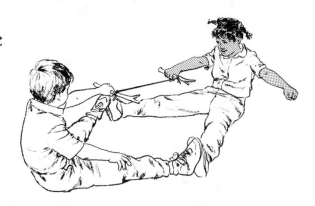

# NATIVE AMERICAN
# ARTS AND CRAFTS

Wherever Native Americans settled, they used what they found in nature to create what they needed in their daily lives. Your students will enjoy making Native American crafts using both natural and manufactured materials. In the following pages, you'll find instructions for creating a cornhusk doll, a drum, a rattle, and paints made from plant dyes.

# Making a Cornhusk Doll

Many Native American children played with cornhusk dolls and animals. Have students make their own dolls or animals.

## Materials:

| | | |
|---|---|---|
| dry cornhusks | cloth scraps | string |
| corn silk | glue | paints |
| cotton balls | bowl of water | paintbrushes |

## What students do:

1. Soak the husks in water for an hour.

2. To make the body, fold three cornhusks of equal length in half.

3. To make the head, place a cotton ball inside the fold and tie a piece of string just below.

4. To make the arms and hands, cut two cornhusks into 5-inch (12.5 cm) lengths. Then tie a piece of string about 1/2 inch (1.2 cm) from each end. Put the arms through the husk body. Tie a piece of string around the body just below the arms to make the waist and to hold the arms in place.

5. To make legs, cut the cornhusk body lengthwise to just below the waist. Tie a piece of string about 1/2 inch (1.2 cm) from each end to make feet.

6. Paint a face and glue on corn silk for hair.

7. Use material scraps to make clothes.

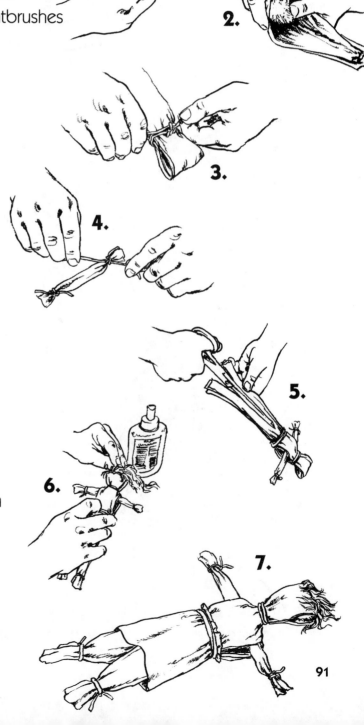

91

# Making a Drum

Music was important in Native American life. The people used drums to accompany singers and to mark time for dance steps. Show students the pictures of Native American drums. Then have them make their own drums.

## Materials:

large coffee cans
pieces of old inner tubes
heavy-duty scissors

**2. & 3.**

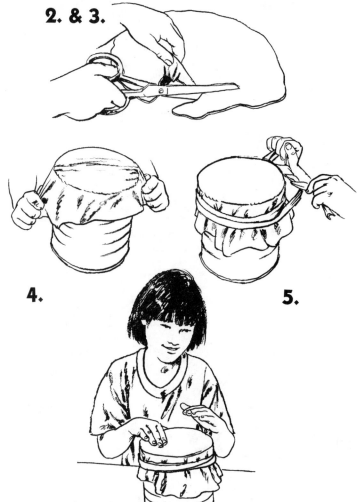

**4.**

**5.**

## What students do:

**1.** Remove the cover from a large can.

**2.** Cut a circle out of the inner tube so that it is about 4 inches (about 10 cm) larger than the opening of the can.

**3.** Cut a strip out of the inner tube long enough to wrap around the can three times.

**4.** Stretch the circular piece of inner tube tightly over the open end of the can to make the drumhead. For an interesting sound, put some water in the can before adding the drumhead.

**5.** Using the strip of inner tube, bind and tie the drumhead as tightly as possible.

Have students use a wooden spoon or a drumstick as a beater. They can also make one by rounding one end of a stick with a piece of sandpaper.

# Making a Rattle

The rattle was another rhythm instrument that Native Americans used. Rattles were made from a variety of materials including bark, turtle shells, horn, and gourds. Have students make their own gourd rattles.

## Materials:

several gourds
   (Prepare gourds for students ahead of time by soaking them in water for several hours, cutting out a hole in each one with a knife, scraping the insides with a spoon, and drying for use.)
scissors
masking tape
small stones, seeds, dry beans, rice
markers
paints and paintbrushes

## What students do:

**1.** Fill the gourd with stones, seeds, beans, or rice.

**2.** Use strips of masking tape to cover the opening.

**3.** Decorate the rattle with paint or markers. Use the rattle and drum to perform the Friendship Dance.

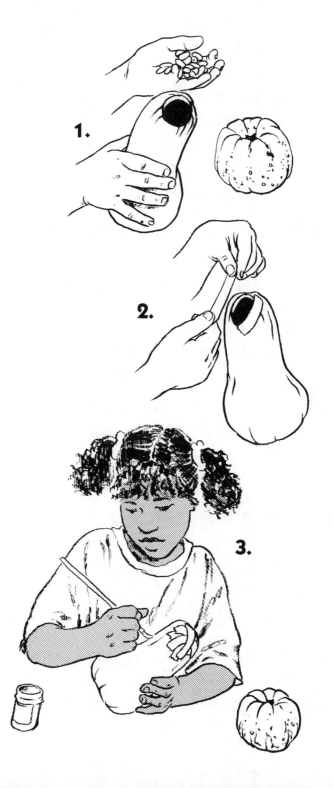

# Making Paints from Plant Parts

Native Americans used berries, roots, leaves, bark, flowers, shells, seeds, skins, and stalks to make dyes and paints.  Have students make their own colors.

If possible, take students on a nature walk to collect plant materials.  They'll need containers or bags.  Students can also bring the following items from their home or neighborhood:
tree bark, walnut shells, cranberries, beets, onion skins, marigold or dandelion flowers, parsley and spinach leaves, blueberries and blackberries, tea bags.

## Materials:

water
bark or nutshells
plant materials
cooking pots and lids
strainer and bowl
food jars
hot plate
hammer or rock
old cloth or rags

## What students do:

**1.** Make a bag out of cloth or rags.

**2.** Pound bark or nutshells into small pieces with a rock or hammer.  Put pieces inside cloth bag.

**3.** Sort out flowers, leaves, stems, berries, and skins by color.  They can be put in the pot as is.

**4.** Put plant parts of a similar color or the bag of bark or nutshells in a pot.

**5.** Add two parts water for one part of plant material and cover the pot with a lid.

**6.** When the mixture boils, lower the heat and let it simmer until it reaches the color you want.

**7.** After the mixture cools, strain it into a bowl.

**8.** Pour the dyes into jars and store until needed.  Use the dyes to make a "Buffalo Skin" picture autobiography. (See page 55.)

Answers to page 95:  1-longhouse; 2-igloo; 3-dugout; 4-snowshoe; 5-hogan; 6-kayak; 7-tipi; 8-wigwam; 9-toboggan; 10-pueblo; 11-bullboat; 12-kachina; 13-chickee; 14-lodge; 15-travois

Name _____ Date _____

# Native American Crossword Puzzle

Complete the crossword below with the names of objects from Native American life.

**ACROSS**

5. Navajo dwelling
8. Lenape dwelling
10. Southwest dwelling
11. Mandan boat
12. Pueblo spirit
13. Seminole dwelling
14. Mandan dwelling
15. Plains carrier

**DOWN**

1. Seneca dwelling
2. Arctic winter dwelling
3. Boat carved from trunk
4. Winter footwear
6. Arctic one-person boat
7. Plains dwelling
9. Type of sled

Answers on page 94.

© 1994 by Troll Associates.

Name _____     Date _____

# Map of North American Tribes

Label and color each Native American cultural region.  Add the names of
tribes you have studied in each region.

© 1994 by Troll Associates.